SPOOKY
the
TEAPOT GHOST

Written by Jennifer Jordan

Illustrated by Ken Morton

Brimax Books · Newmarket · England

Spooky the ghost lived in a big
blue teapot in a garden shed.
It was an old dusty teapot.
It had no lid and a funny spout.
But Spooky liked his cosy home.
No-one knew he lived there.
He could fly around all day
and no-one could see him.

But Spooky had no friends.
"No-one knows who I am," he said.
"No-one can see a ghost."
He went to the park and fed the ducks.
He sat on the swings
and slid down the slide.
Then he threw a ball for a dog.
But no-one spoke to him.
No-one knew he was there.

One day he flew out of his teapot.
He flew over the town and over the fiel[d]
He sat in a tree in Dapple Wood.
It was sports day and all the animals
were having fun.
"Maybe I can have some fun too,"
said Spooky. "No-one can see me,
so I can play some tricks."

First it was the running race.
The animals stood in a line
waiting for the race to begin.
"Ready . . . Steady . . . Go!"
All the animals fell over.
"Who said that?" asked Miffy Mouse.
They looked all around them
but no-one could see Spooky
in the tree.

Then it was the high jump.
Miffy Mouse fixed a long pole
between two trees.
But Spooky moved the pole.
He moved it far too high
and no-one could jump over it.
"Who moved the pole?"
asked Miffy Mouse.
They looked up in the trees.
But no-one could see Spooky the ghost.

The sack race was next.
But Spooky moved the finishing post
in to the middle of Dapple Stream!
All the animals were very wet
and very cross.
''Someone is playing tricks on us,''
said Miffy Mouse. But no-one
could see Spooky. He waved goodbye
as he flew home to his big blue teapot.

That night Oscar Owl tapped on the window of the garden shed.
"You played those tricks, Spooky," he said. "I know it was you."
Spooky peeped out of his teapot.
"I am a ghost," said Spooky.
"You cannot see me."
"I cannot see you in the daytime," said Oscar. "But you glow in the dark, so I can see you now!"

Oscar Owl was very kind. Spooky said
he was sorry for playing tricks.
''Then come to Dapple Wood with me,'
said Oscar. They flew off
into the dark sky.
''I have never been out in the dark
before,'' said Spooky. ''Look, I really
am glowing!''
The streets and fields lit up
as Spooky flew by.

The animals in Dapple Wood were wide awake.
Spooky and Oscar flew down beside them, Spooky saw that the animals looked sad.
''What is the matter?'' he asked.
''We cannot leave the wood,'' said Mr Mole.
''We would get lost in the dark,'' said Boris Badger.
''So we never have any fun,'' said Rosie Rabbit.

"Come with me," said Spooky.
He led the animals to the garden shed.
"I have never been out of the wood
before," said Rosie Rabbit.
"We cannot get lost," said Mr Mole.
"Spooky is glowing like a torch."
"We will take my teapot back
to Dapple Wood," said Spooky.
"Then we can have some fun."
The animals pushed and pulled
the teapot back to Dapple Wood.
They were all puffing.
"This is not fun," said Boris Badger.

Back in Dapple Wood they pushed
the teapot into Dapple Stream.
''All aboard!'' said Spooky.
But as the animals climbed onto
the teapot, it began to wobble.
''Help!'' called Mr Mole. ''I am
going to fall!''
Splash! Mr Mole fell in to Dapple Strea
Boris Badger and Rosie Rabbit
pulled him out.
''Now I am all wet,'' said Mr Mole.
''Never mind,'' said Spooky. ''Now we
are going on an adventure!''

They sailed down the stream to the rive
Very soon they were sailing on the sea.
They sailed up and down on the waves.
The big blue teapot landed on a beach.
Spooky and the animals played on
the sand and looked for seashells.
''This is such fun!'' said Rosie Rabbit.

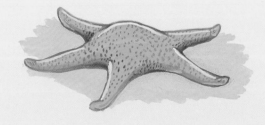

The next morning they sailed home.
The big blue teapot was warm and dry
in a tree trunk. Spooky slept all day.
Every night he stayed awake
with his new friends.
They had such fun sailing away
in the big blue teapot.
"It is nice being a ghost after all,"
said Spooky.

Say these words again.

cosy

tricks

running

sack

waved

window

playing

glowing

streets

wood

torch

puffing

garden

sailing